VISUAL ILLUSIONS

T&J

This edition published 2011

Published by
TAJ BOOKS INTERNATIONAL LLP
27 Ferndown Gardens
Cobham
Surrey
KT11 2BH
UK
www.tajbooks.com

ISBN: 978-1-84406-173-0

VISUAL ILLUSIONS

VISUAL ILLUSIONS

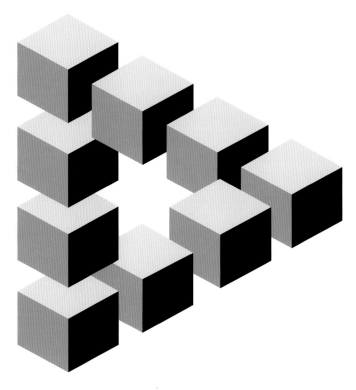

James Kingston

INTRODUCTION

Optical illusions are all to do with the mind and how the brain processes and makes sense of the information it receives. Many scientists, particularly those working in the fields of psychology and optics, have spent their careers investigating the way this information is processed and often the only way they can produce physical proof of their work is to construct an optical illusion which uses the properties they describe. In this way many optical illusions are named after their creator. An illusion is a phenomenon in which the physical dimensions or properties of an object or image are different from its appearance because the eyes and brain are fooled into "seeing" something that is not there. Optical illusions occur because our brain is trying to make sense of what our eyes see, even at the expense of our conscious brain knowing that what we see is an illusion. As the examples in this book show, even when the brain knows it is being fooled, it is still fooled into seeing what isn't there. There are good scientific explanations for many illusions, but intriguingly, some illusional effects still baffle scientists as to how they work to deceive the brain. Interestingly, not everyone will be able to see any given illusion, a mystery which scientists are unable to explain. Optical illusions fall into three broad categories:

- Physiological illusions are a reaction to excessive stimulation—color, brightness, movement, and tilt—on the eyes and brain.
- Cognitive illusions occur when the interface between the eyes and the brain jumps to conclusions about what is actually there, instead of actually seeing what is there.
- Literal optical illusions deceive the eye and brain into seeing an image that isn't there.

The Eye

The brain is a sealed unit relying entirely on the body's senses to supply it with information—taste, touch, sight, sound, and smell: anything to do with vision is supplied with information via the eyes. Babies are said to be short-sighted for a few months after birth; this is not strictly speaking true. Babies can, in fact, see perfectly well but their brains do not yet possess enough information to process and understand what they see. Colors and shapes, near and far, blur into one until the baby's brain learns to understand the signals the eyes are sending. So, from our earliest days our brains learn to interpret the information relayed to it by the eyes and this is how optical illusions work: they fool the brain into interpreting and "seeing" an image which is not there.

The eye is an organ which detects light and objects then sends the signals through the optic nerve to the brain. Human eyes distinguish shape and color and thanks to binocular vision, depth perception as well. Simply put, light reaches the inside of the eye through the cornea at the front of the eye; the light then moves through the pupil which expands and contracts with varying light levels.

The eye is a complicated visual-sense organ and comprises a sphere 80% of which is composed of vitreous humor, behind a transparent front portion which holds the aqueous humor. Its movement is governed by muscles. The amount of light which reaches the retina is controlled by the iris which expands in minimal light and contracts in bright light, a reaction which is most often compared to the way a shutter works on a camera.

INTRODUCTION

Inside the eye in the bacillary layer lie the rods and cones; the rods perceive light levels and only really work well at low light levels. The cones are color sensitive and need higher levels of light for perception; there are three types of cones, those which are sensitive to long-wavelength (reds), medium-wavelength (greens), and short-wavelength (blues). Rods and cones are connected by nerve fibers to the optic nerve which in turn sends impulses in the form of electrical signals to the brain for interpretation. A common aspect of illusion is caused by color perception and the way exactly the same color appears either lighter or darker depending on its neighboring or surrounding color. This is because the brain makes assumptions about color relative to its surroundings.

Brief History of Optical Illusion

There are thousands of examples of optical illusions—or camouflage—in the natural world. Many have evolved out of the survival instinct which encourages an animal to hide from its predators by imitating its surroundings or a similar, but dangerous, species. Hunters—animal and human—have used camouflage for centuries so they can creep up on their prey or lie in wait without detection, but the use of camouflageby military forces is, surprisingly, a later phenomenon. It was more important to be able to distinguish friend from foe or to stand out and intimidate the enemy with bright military uniforms rather than fight unseen for many centuries. The use of military camouflage by European troops only started in the 18th century with the Jäger riflemen who adopted solemn shades of gray and green so they could hide from the enemy; the art of camouflage was also an important factor in favor of American troops in the years before and after the revolution. It was only at the turn of the 20th century that the armies of most countries changed their uniform to drab colors so their soldiers could merge into their surroundings.

Most camouflage works by imitating the colors and shapes of the surrounding terrain so that the camouflaged person, building, or vehicle almost literally disappears into its surroundings. Taken out of context, however, camouflage works the opposite way. Take dazzle camouflage—an interesting development for naval warfare used by the Royal Navy during World War 1. The scheme is credited to the artist Norman Wilkinson (1878–1971); he was not attempting to hide the vessel (not possible with a huge, smoke-belching vessel) but rather break up its form and confuse the viewer. The designs were devised by artists and then rendered onto the vessels in wide jagged lines of complex geometric patterns and contrasting colors. The viewer, especially from a distance in a submarine, wasn't sure whether the vessel was advancing or receding, which way it was moving, how big it was, and how many vessels were actually there. Close-up, however, dazzle made the vessel more obvious.

Artists and Illusion

Many artists have used illusion in their works to show off their skills and wit, and sometimes to hide cryptic messages within their work. One of the earliest and best known examples is Hans Holbein's distorted skull—called an anamorphic—in The Ambassadors, (1533). To see the skull properly the viewer has to look at the image up close from the side. Nobody knows why Holbein placed it in the painting other than to show off his skill. A nice suggestion is that the painting was intended to hang in a stairwell and the skull would jump out at the viewer and startle them as they walked up the stairs.

Trompe l'oeil (illusion painting—literally fooling the eye) is an old painting trick which became much more sophisticated in the Renaissance, when the science of perspective started to be properly understood. Artists like Andrea Mantegna (c. 1431–1506) painting ceilings using illusionary techniques such as foreshortening to imply vast space above the images. This is known as di sotto in sù, meaning "upward" in Italian as the viewer was always below the painting.

Perhaps the greatest exploitation of optical illusion was the 17th century art explosion called Baroque when trompe l'oeil was used extensively to represent elaborate decoration. This was very much an Italian religious style and was only really seen to any extent there and in southern Germany. It uses illusion perspective to fool the viewer into thinking they are seeing a three-dimensional image and was especially used in murals and for decorating the high ceilings and walls of palaces and churches.

Artists enjoy playing with their viewers' minds and further fashions in trompe l'oeil include quodlibet in which everyday items such as playing cards, notes, pens, musical instruments, etc are scattered in an alcove or on a wall and are only discovered for being painted on closer inspection. In recent decades trompe l'oeil have appeared on the sides of buildings in towns and cities around the world, often transforming the urban landscape with their fantasies.

In the early Renaissance the strange Italian artist Giuseppe Arcimboldo (1527–1593) used compositions of fruit, vegetables, flowers and other objects to produce grotesque faces and figures. He became an influence on the Surrealist artists, in particular

Salvador Dali (1904–1989) who frequently explored distortion and illusion in his works. The other Surrealists, such as Marcel Duchamp (1887–1968), also used illusion as part of the most fundamental aspects of their work. The American artist Charles Allan Gilbert (1873–1929) in his day was a well known artist and illustrator whose painting All is Vanity is an optical illusion of alternately a skull and a woman sitting at her vanity desk.

The Op Art (short for optical art) movement in the 1960s explored the mind altering effects of color and shape. An exhibition held at the Museum of Modern Art in New York in 1965 called "The Responsive Eye" brought the attention of the public to the movement with the work of artists such as Frank Stella, Tony DeLap, Bridget Riley, and the Anonima group whose works appear to distort and move within their canvases' and played games with visual perception.

M.C.Escher

The artist who played with optical illusions more cleverly and consistently than anyone else was the Dutch artist Maurits Cornelis Escher. He was a stunning graphic illustrator who would get frustrated at his inability to work out a particular visual idea or puzzle. He would wrestle with the problem, even losing sleep in the process, until he worked out how to do it, which sometimes necessitated making a 3-D model so he could work out the angles, vanishing points, and other details. Escher was not obviously a mathematician, but when he showed his brother Beer, a professor of geology at Leiden University, his latest drawings which explored the regular division of the plane—inspired by Islamic tile patterns in the Alhambra palace—his brother immediately saw the connection between Escher's work and crystallography. He recommended a number of articles on the subject and Escher became enthralled by the principles of symmetry and how he could use it in his work.

Escher's extensive notebooks filled with his ideas and calculations prove that he had taught himself into becoming a significant research mathematician: he had unknowingly studied areas of crystallography years ahead of any professional mathematician. With such analytical precision Escher played with vision, space, and perspective, earning the attention of mathematicians and philosophers with his impossible structures and puzzling but apparently logical drawings. In the early 1950s Escher became obsessed with the notion of an endless staircase and started working on what would become some of his most famous works such as House of Stairs which started with the basis of the Penrose Triangle, and the complex Relativity which features three stairways intertwined in three different gravity planes, and Ascending and Descending which uses visual paradox to depict a never-ending staircase.

Start of Modern Optical Illusion

The father of modern optical illusion is the multi-skilled Austrian scientist and mathematical genius Hermann von Helmholtz. Born in Potsdam, Prussia, in 1821 into an intellectual family, he was well educated especially in classical languages and philosophy. Although principally interested in physics, he studied medicine instead at the Friedrich Wilhelm Medical Institute in Berlin because his education was provided free of charge provided he served for eight years as an army doctor; however, he was still able to attend the physics lectures. On graduation in 1843 Helmholtz was assigned to a regiment back home in Potsdam where, using his bountiful free time, he set up a laboratory at the barracks.

Helmholtz's scientific abilities were soon noticed and he was released from his military obligations to allow him to pursue an academic career which peaked when he was appointed first professor of physics at the University of Berlin in 1871 and then in 1888 on his appointment as first director of the Physico-Technical Institute in Berlin. Through his researches and investigations Helmholtz made many scientific advances, not least the development of the ophthalmoscope and the ophthalmometer (in 1851).

In 1856 he published the first volume of his most important work, the Handbook of Physiological Optics, which called on his physiological investigations, philosophical insights, precision mathematical skills, and thorough understanding of physics to expound his rejection of nature philosophy (in which scientific conclusions were drawn from philosophical ideas as espoused by Kant, rather than from empirical evidence collated from observations of the natural world). Much of his energy was then directed towards the study of optics and understanding how the mind learns anything at all about the outside world when it has to rely solely on what the eyes tell it.

Using his ophthalmoscope Helmholtz started studying physiological optics, specifically color vision and dioptrics (the study of the refraction of light), especially with regard to lenses and distortion. Through his study of the eye and its relationship to the brain Helmholtz became the first person to describe illusions as unconscious inferences from sensory data and earlier learned knowledge—in other words, that the brain predicts what is is seeing and accepts it as reality, when in fact it is an illusion.

Helmholtz demonstrated this using illusory stripes: he drew two identical squares and showed that the square area appears to be wider when vertical lines are drawn on it, but when horizontal lines are drawn over the area it appears taller. This has become known as the Helmholtz Illusion and has been referenced by Richard Gregory as being the foundation of his research into optical illusions.

With his opthalmoscope Helmholtz could show the living retina and the interior of the eye and reveal diseases therein, something never before seen. For this he was honored in 1882 by Kaiser Wilhelm I who elevated him to the nobility and allowed him to use the suffix "von" with his name. His name (without the suffix) lives on through the Helmholtz Association research centers, currently the largest scientific organization in Germany.

Matthew Luckiesh (1883–1967) was another important visual pioneer and researcher in light and vision and was known to his peers as the "Father of the Science of Seeing." He wrote Visual Illusions: Their Causes, Characteristics and Applications, the seminal work on optical illusion published in 1922 and one of the first comprehensive books on the subject. During World War I Luckiesh studied the effects of camouflaging and went on to design camouflage for ships and planes using visual illusion techniques. After the war he went to work for the General Electric Company in East Cleveland, Ohio, where he was director of the Nela Lighting Research Laboratory. While studying the effects of light and seeing, he developed a number of lamps including the hugely successful MAZDA Flametint Lamp of which some 13 million were sold in 1929. Another of his important developments was the MAZDA Daylight Lamp which replicates average daylight colors and tones and was popularly used by artists and throughout department stores.

Between 1911 and 1960 Luckiesh wrote 28 books and some 860 technical and scientific articles explaining his theories about light, vision, and other related aspects of lighting, as well as his ideas about color and its psychological effects on people; furthermore he registered 11 U.S. patents.

Scientists and their Illusions

A physiological illusion works when the eye looks at a fixed point within the image and after a short period of time the repetitive stimulation to the receptors creates an afterimage which provides the illusion of change. With a physiological illusion lines or colors appear to flicker, change, produce ghost images,and even disappear altogether. The effect can leave the viewer feeling slightly dizzy and disorientated for a period.

German speech scientist and influential physiologist Ludimar Hermann (1838–1914) devised the Herman Grid Illusion, a classic physiological illusion, which works through receptive fields and lateral inhibition. To achieve the effect, excitation synapses in the eye are stimulated by light and increase their neural activity at the same time as inhibitory synapses decrease neural activity. The result of this (for most observers) are dark blobs in the white spaces between the grid lines.

The Herman Grid was taken a step further by E.Lingelbach in 1994 when he produced the Scintillating Grid variation : the grid remains the same but here the intersections are a pale gray with a white dot superimposed in the center of each intersection. When looked at generally, the white dots, and now black dots as well, seem to appear and disappear at random, however, the black dot does not appear when the section is stared at directly.

INTRODUCTION

In the late 1960s the Cornsweet Illusion (aka Craik-O'Brien-Cornsweet Illusion —see page 42) was expanded on by Tom Cornsweet after earlier observations from Craik and O'Brien. Dr. Tom Cornsweet is Emeritus Professor of Cognitive Sciences, Electrical and Computer Engineering and Ophthalmology at the University of California. His illusion plays with luminescence and the way the brain interprets the same color shade differently depending on its surroundings. Cornsweet was able to explain the science behind the illusion by showing how light acts on the cones and rods in the retina which produce the illusion. The critical point has become known as the "Cornsweet Edge" and has to do with luminescent gradients and contrast.

The McCollough Effect is named after Celeste McCollough, an American scientist researching human visual perception. In 1965 she discovered the effect which is the result of a phenomenon called the contingent after effect. Through a process known as induction (or adaptation) a person alternately views differently colored vertical and horizontal gratings then looks at a black and white version of the same grid lines, these will then appear to be a paler version of the same colors. The effect will occur with any pair of colors but is most pronounced when the colors are complementary, such as red and green or orange and blue; also when the spatial frequency is exactly the same for all the grids. The effects of such induction can last for a remarkably long time; researchers have shown that for ten minutes adaptation the aftereffects can persist for 24 hours and in some cases for days and even weeks longer.

McCollough discovered the effect during a sabbatical from the Department of Psychology at Oberlin College, while conducting tests to see what happens to eyesight when wearing glasses tinted with two colors. She published her findings in a paper which encouraged other visual specialists to investigate the phenomenon. She later researched the problems inherent in night vision equipment. In the 1980s the McCollough Effect was reported by people doing word processing on computer monitors which used colored phosphor text, particularly green against a black background, and then tried to read a book with text of the same spatial frequency, and found that the letters looked pink.

Cognitive illusions

Cognitive illusions generally appear as first one thing and then on adjusting your focus appear as another. There are four principal types of cognitive illusion:

Ambiguous illusion such as the Necker Cube and the Rubin Vase . This latter is one of the best known cognitive optical illusions and was developed by Danish phenomenologist and psychologist Edgar John Rubin, (1886–1951). He worked in the area of figure ground perception and devised the Vase in about 1915 and published a two-volume work—Visual Figures—in which other illusions demonstrated the principle that the figure and ground can be reversed. Each of the images is valid, the symmetrical profiles and the vase, but it is impossible to view them simultaneously: the brain has to flick from one view to the other.

Distorting illusions play with the use of parallel lines in such illusions as the simple Müller-Lyer Illusionwhere lines drawn like arrows appear to be of different lengths. English experimental psychologist Dr Richard Gregory is an expert on artificial intelligence and optical illusions and has written widely on both subjects. He is Emeritus Professor of Neuropsychology at the University of Bristol and was the first to notice and describe the Café Wall Illusion , which he saw on a café wall in Bristol. The illusion is created by horizontal parallel lines composed of alternating black and white bricks which appear to make the lines waver and bend.

Karl Ewald Hering (1834–1918) was a German physiologist who researched into spatial perception and color vision. He discovered that two vertical lines can appear to be bending outwards if they are superimposed over a lined or patterned background, in turn this creates a feeling of perspective and a false impression of depth, this is now called the Hering Illusion.

The German astrophysicist Johann Zöllner(1834–1882) was controversial professor of physics and astronomy at the University of Leipzig. He also studied transcendental physics and optical illusions which brought him ridicule from some of his peers. However his name lives on through the Zöllner Illusion (see page 108) in which apparent diagonal lines are actually parallel and for his contributions to astrophysics a crater on the Moon is named after him.

The Poggendorff Illusion (see page 96) was discovered by German physicist J.C.Poggendorff in 1860 after he received a letter from Zöller describing an illusion he noticed on some fabric in which parallel lines lying over short diagonal lines appeared to be misaligned. Johann Christian Poggendorff(1796–1877) was the editor of "Annalen der Physik und Chemie," the leading scientific journal of the time, for 52 years as well as being a researcher into electricity and magnetism. He devised the mirror galvanometer, a machine which uses a mirror to sense electric current.

Another distorting illusion is called the Sander Illusion—aka Sander's Parallelogram— and was described by the German psychologist Friedrich Sander (1889–1971) in 1926, a researcher at the Leipzig Institute of Experimental Psychology/Psychological Institute. In 1929 he became professor in Giessen.

In the 19th century German medical doctor and psychologist Wilhelm Wundt invented an illusion which became known as the Wundt Illusion (see page 106). He is now accorded the honor of being one of the founding figures of modern psychology and credited with being the father of experimental psychology.

Wundt founded one of the world's first purpose-built psychological research laboratories at the University of Leipzig. With university resources behind him Wundt was able to establish psychology as a distinct science in its own right. Over a 65-year career in psychology Wundt produced a prolific number of writings on all aspects of his chosen field and helped to teach the next generation of outstanding psychologists. His particular areas of interest were the identification of mental disorders, the nature of religious belief, and abnormal behavior. He also attempted to produce a map of the damaged parts of the human brain and started the first journal for psychological research in 1881.

American experimental psychologist Joseph Jastrow, (1863–1944) like many of the other important visual scientists, made his living in scientific fields other than optics, specifically the evolution of language, but also worked on visual problems and optical illusions as a sideline. In 1900 he served for a year as the president of the American Psychological Association. He was fascinated by mental processes and devised a number of visual illusions which played with perception and actuality and has the Jastrow Illusion named after him.

The Italian psychologist Mario Ponzo (1882–1960) specialized in vision and optical

INTRODUCTION

illusions and first demonstrated the Ponzo Illusion in 1913, in which perspective tricks the brain into believing that the line in the foreground is shorter than the apparently receding line: it is about placing an object out of context which fools the brain to revert to expectations (learned history). For this illusion the mind decides the size of the object based entirely on the background. The illusion disappears if the diagram is turned upside down. This is also given as the explanation for why the Moon appears bigger when it is near the horizon rather than overhead high in the sky.

Paradox illusions

Paradox illusions show an impossible image which upon examination cannot be faulted. The master of this type of illusion was the self-taught mathematician and graphic artist M.C. Escher who played with cognitive misunderstanding to play the illusional trick of never-ending staircases and waterfalls in perpetual motion.

The Necker Cube was devised by the Swiss crystallographer Louis Albert Necker (1786–1861) in 1832. This plays with two-dimensional shadows on a three-dimensional object and works especially successfully with a cube. Here there are no perspectives to help the brain orientate the image and so it is termed an ambiguous image and the cube itself, an impossible object. When the cube is stared at it will appear to work in one way and then another and be perfectly valid in both, this is known as multistable perception. The illustrator M.C. Escher visually played with the ambiguity of the image and used the impossible cube as the basis for a number of illustrations, particularly his lithograph Belvedere.

Another impossible object is used by Escher in his extraordinary lithograph called Waterfall. The object has since become known as the Penrose Triangle, or Penrose Tribar. First devised by the English mathematician Roger Penrose (b. 1931) in the 1950s, the triangle appears solid but cannot exist. It was created for real as an optical illusion sculpture in 1934 by the Swedish artist Oscar Reutersvärd, and stands in East Perth, Western Australia. Penrose is a mathematical physicist with a highly distinguished career, who proved, among many other significant things, that singularities such as black holes are formed from the gravitational collapse of vast, dying stars.

Distorting Illusions

Distorting illusions such as The False Spiral or Fraser Spiral Illusion —aka Twisted Cord Illusion— comprises a series of concentric circles which appear to be spirals. The illusion was first described by British psychologist James Fraser in 1908. The eye perceives phantom twists and deviations because of the sequence of twisted elements, the effect is heightened by the background, which is most effective when it is checkered.

The Adelson Checker Illusion —aka Same Color Illusion—shows that our brains automatically think in 3-D rather than just relay what the eyes tell it . It was devised by Edward H Adelson, Professor of Vision Science in the Department of Brain and Cognitive Sciences at MIT in 1995. Professor Adelson studies human and machine vision, including material perception and motion analysis, and has published extensively in his fields. He has devised many visual illusions which demonstrate how shade perception alters depending on the background.

INTRODUCTION

Fictional illusions

Fictional illusions are defined as hallucinations and seen by only one person, usually a schizophrenic or someone who has taken a hallucinogen. They are not relevant to the science of optical illusions.

Gestalt Theory of Perception

The first psychologists to systematically study perceptual organization coined the term Gestalt Theory to explain their ideas and one of their first studies was into ways of seeing and understanding, especially illusion. Leading members were Johan Wolfgang von Goethe, Ernst Mach, Christian von Ehrenfels, Max Wertheimer, Wolfgang Köhler, Kurt Koffka, and Kurt Lewin. They were all Germans working in the 1920s and many of them were forced to flee to America when their work became labeled as subversive during the Nazi era. Gestalt Theory is best described as the way of looking at an object and breaking it down into its individual parts, although the viewer is not aware of the different pieces when looking at the whole. There are six principles of Gestalt perception: proximity, similarity, common fate, good continuation, closure, and area and symmetry.

The Austrian physicist and philosopher Ernst Mach (1838–1916) is best known for his speed scale applied to the velocity of an object moving through the air, usually of planes or rockets, in which, for example, subsonic is expressed as Ma ‹ 1 and supersonic 1.2 ‹ Ma ‹ 5. However, Ernst Mach also gives his name to the optical illusion known as Mach Bands . These comprise two wide bands, one lighter than the other, separated by a narrow third strip which gradates vertically from light to dark which the human eye sees as two narrow bands of differing brightnesses. This effect is probably due to an effect known as lateral inhibition (put simplistically, an excited neuron is able to reduce its neighbors activity and therefore they can't "see"). The brain interprets the Mach Bands as a group of varying contrast vertical bands which it then calculates as lines of contrast relative to its neighbor stripe. The exterior stripes have less lateral inhibition so appear to be darker or lighter than they really are and therefore more obvious than the stripes in the center.

Walter H. Ehrenstein (1950–2009) was a research assistant at Dortmund university in the Institute for Occupational Physiology. The illusion which bears his namein which the sides of a square placed inside a pattern of concentric circles appears to be curved. Ehrenstein was a Gestalt psychologist.

Gaetano Kanizsa was an Italian psychologist and founder of the Institute of Psychology of Trieste as well as being an amateur artist. He started his academic career with a thesis about eidetic memory and served for 30 years as a professor at Trieste. He was the first psychologist to describe what became known as the Kanizsa Triangle, in which there appears to be a white triangle, although none exists, . The contours of the triangle are illusory and are created by the brain in an attempt to understand the diagram. This type of illusion is called a subjective or illusory contour and is a reductionist analysis of vision and part of the Gestalt theory of perception.

AFTERIMAGE ILLUSION

An afterimage or ghost image is an illusion that refers to an image continuing to appear in one's vision after the exposure to the original has ceased. One of the most common afterimages is the bright glow that seems to float before one's eyes after staring at a light bulb or a headlight for a few seconds.

Afterimages come in two forms, negative (inverted) and positive (retaining original color).

Negative Afterimages

Negative afterimages are caused when the eye's photoreceptors adapt from over stimulation and lose sensitivity. Normally the eye deals with this problem by rapidly moving small amounts, the motion later being "filtered out" so it is not noticeable. If the colour image is large enough that the small movements are not enough to change the color under one area of the retina, those cones will eventually tire or adapt and stop responding. The rod cells can also be affected by this.

When the eyes are then diverted to a blank space, the adapted photoreceptors send out a weak signal and those colors remain muted. However, the surrounding cones that were not being excited by that colour are still "fresh", and send out a strong signal. The signal is exactly the same as if looking at the opposite color, which is how the brain interprets it.

▶**Stare at this image for 10 seconds then look at a blank white surface**

22

BEZOLD EFFECT

The Bezold effect is named after a German professor of meteorology, Wilhelm von Bezold (1837-1907), who discovered that a color may appear different depending on its relation to adjacent colors. It happens when small areas of color are interspersed, an assimilation effect called the von Bezold spreading effect similar to spatial color mixing is achieved. The opposite effect is observed when large areas of color are placed adjacent to each other, resulting in color contrast.

Description

When looking at a specific hue, it can appear to change in appearance depending on the colors that surround it. For example, a yellow box surrounded by blue will look darker than a yellow box surrounded by red. Often, the surrounded color seems to take on a tint of the color that surrounds it; red boxes surrounded by blue will appear more bluish than those surrounded by white.

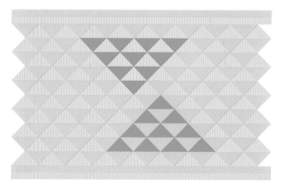

◀ In this pattern, the green triangles make the surrounded yellow triangles seem darker. Conversely, the green triangles in the lower part appear lighter.

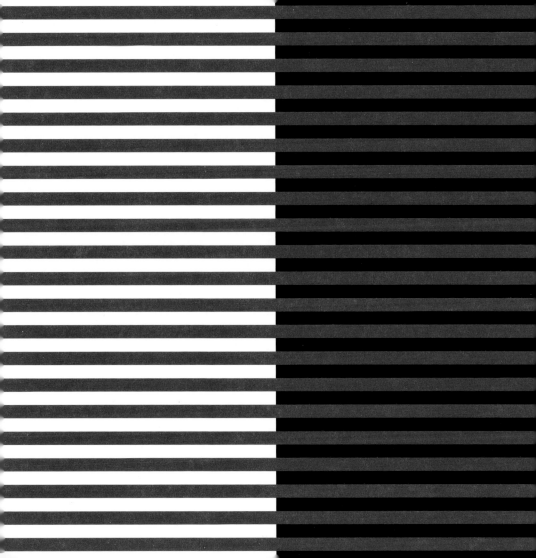

BLIVET

A blivet, also known as an "impossible fork," is an optical illusion and an impossible object. It appears to have three cylindrical prongs at one end which then mysteriously transform into two rectangular prongs at the other end. Often, upon first glance, the blivet looks entirely possible, but upon closer inspection quickly becomes undecipherable.

The blivet is often cited as having various origins. Many claim that it originated as an illustration on the cover of the March 1965 issue of Mad Magazine, from a contributer who claimed the illustration was original. It was later discovered that the figure had been previously published in several aviation, engineering, and science-fiction periodicals during May and June of the previous year. Also in 1964, D.H. Schuster published the figure in an article for the American Journal of Psychology, leading many to refer to the figure as a "Schuster Fork." Some erroneously refer to artist M.C. Escher when discussing the origins of the blivet; this is most likely due to the fact that Escher is famous for works that contain similar optical illusions.

The blivet makes clever use of visual perspective to create the illusion. Lines that extend from one side are joined together at the opposite end to create the prongs. The longer the prongs of the fork are and the further away from each other the two sides are, the more convincing the illusion becomes.

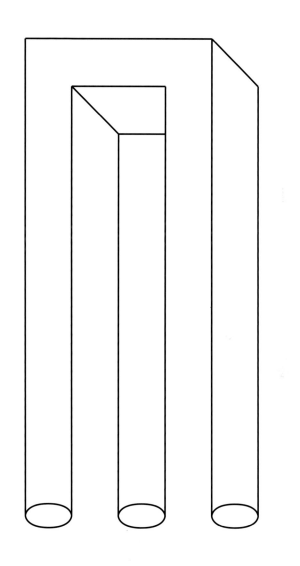

CAFE WALL ILLUSION

The café wall illusion is an illusion first described by Richard Gregory in 1973. According to Gregory, this effect was first observed by a member of his laboratory, Steve Simpson, in the tiles of the wall of a café at the bottom of St Michael's Hill, Bristol. This optical illusion makes the parallel straight horizontal lines appear to be bent. To construct the illusion, alternating light and dark "bricks" are laid in staggered rows. It is essential for the illusion that each "brick" is surrounded by a layer of "mortar" (the grey in the image). This should ideally be of a colour in between the dark and light colour of the "bricks".

▲ The Port 1010 building in Melbourne Harbour, Australia

CHUBB ILLUSION

The Chubb illusion is an optical illusion wherein the apparent contrast of a patterned object varies dramatically, depending on the context of the presentation.

The phenomenon was first observed by Charles Chubb and colleagues Sperling and Solomon, who published their findings in the December 1989 edition of Proceedings of the National Academy of Sciences USA in an article entitled "Texture interactions determine perceived contrast".

To illustrate the Chubb illusion, a circle of low contrast texture or pattern is placed in two different fields. When placed in a plain gray field, the circle appears to have more contrast than when it is placed in a field that surrounds it with high contrast texture or pattern.

The lower contrast image is perceived to be higher contrast when placed in front of a gray background because the gray background is more ambiguous than the high contrast background. The brain is used to interpreting images that are subject to "imperfect transmittance"; viewing objects from a distance, through fog, or through water or glass are examples of imperfect transmittance. In these cases, the brain compensates for the lower levels of light that actually fall upon the retina in an attempt to judge the true colors or contrast of the object. When placed in front of a gray background, the contrast pattern seems more high contrast because the ambiguous gray background causes the brain to interpret the image using imperfect transmittance. With the high contrast background, it is more obvious that there is nothing hindering the transmittance of light from the image, and the brain perceives the image more accurately.

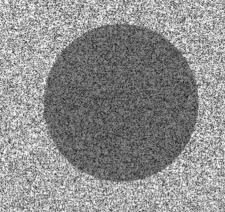

CORNSWEET ILLUSION

The Cornsweet illusion, also known as Craik-O'Brien-Cornsweet illusion or Craik-Cornsweet illusion was described in detail by Tom Cornsweet in the late 1960s. Craik and O'Brien had made earlier observations in a similar vein.

In the image, the entire region to the right of the "edge" in the middle looks slightly lighter than the area to the left of the edge, but in fact the brightness of both areas is exactly the same, as can be seen by blacking out the region containing the edge (see below).

▲ With the center gradient covered, the effect is not visible

DELBOEUF ILLUSION

The Delboeuf illusion is an optical illusion of relative size perception. In the best-known version of the illusion, two circles of identical size are placed near to each other and one is surrounded by an annulus; the surrounded circle then appears larger than the non-surrounded circle if the annulus is close, while appearing smaller than the non-surrounded circle if the annulus is distant. Recent work suggests it is caused by the same visual processes that cause the Ebbinghaus illusion

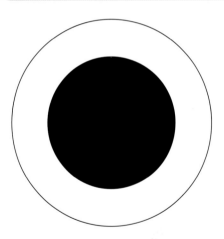 

▲ As the outside circle is larger, the inner circle has the effect of looking smaller

▶ As the outside circle is smaller the inner circle appears to be larger

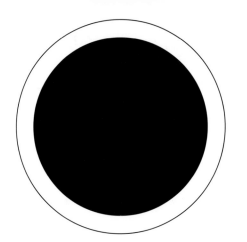

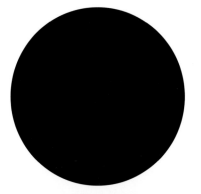

EBBINGHAUS ILLUSION

The Ebbinghaus illusion or Titchener circles is an illusion of relative size perception. In the best-known version of the illusion, two circles of identical size are placed near to each other and one is surrounded by large circles while the other is surrounded by small circles; the first central circle then appears smaller than the second central circle. It was named for its discoverer, the German psychologist Hermann Ebbinghaus (1850-1909) it was popularised in the English-speaking world by Titchener in a 1901 textbook of experimental psychology, hence its alternative name "Titchener circles".

Although commonly thought of as an illusion of size, recent work suggests that the critical factor in the illusion is the distance of the surrounding circles and the completeness of the annulus, making the illusion a variation of the Delboeuf illusion. If the surrounding circles are near to the central circle it appears larger, while if they are far away it appears smaller. Obviously, the size of the surrounding circles dictates how near they can be to the central circle, resulting in many studies confounding the two variables.

EHRENSTEIN ILLUSION

The Ehrenstein illusion is an optical illusion in which a circle appears at the end points of a series of lines. The Ehrenstein illusion is one of the most popular subjective contour illusions—those that create the impression of a shape even though a large portion of the contour is nonexistent.

The "phantom edge phenomena" is due to what neuropsychologists call the "T-effect." Groups of neural cells see breaks in lines, and if given no further input, will assume that there is a figure in front of the lines. Scientists believe that this happens because the brain has been trained to view the break in lines as an object that could pose a potential threat. With a lack of additional information, the brain errs on the side of safety and perceives the space as an object. The circle is the most simple and symmetrical object, so the mind usually sees a circle unless active effort is made to see an alternate shape.

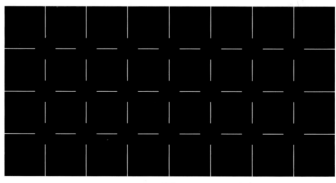

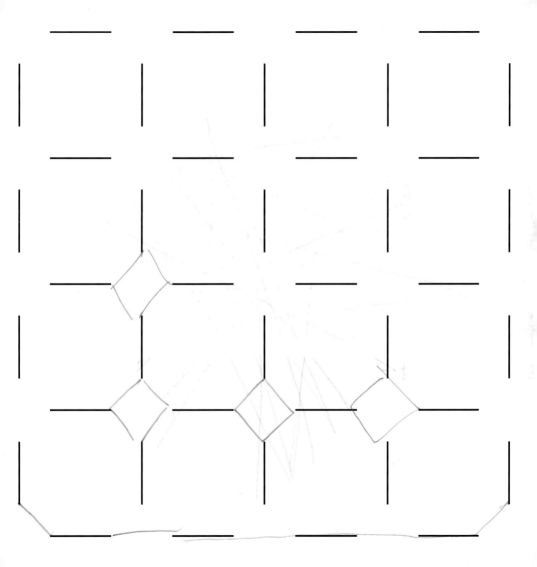

EHRENSTEIN ILLUSION

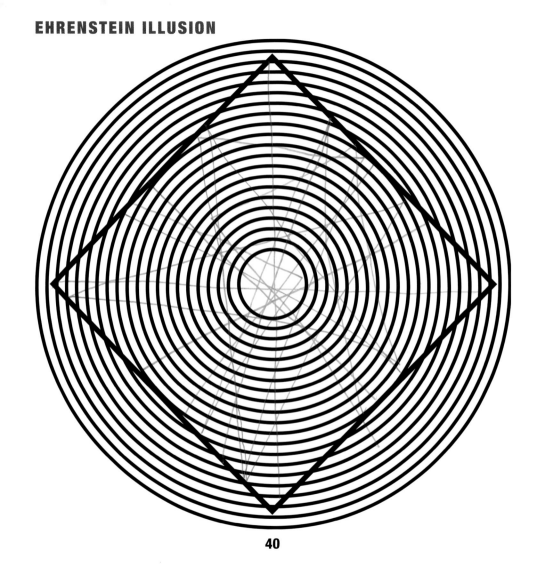

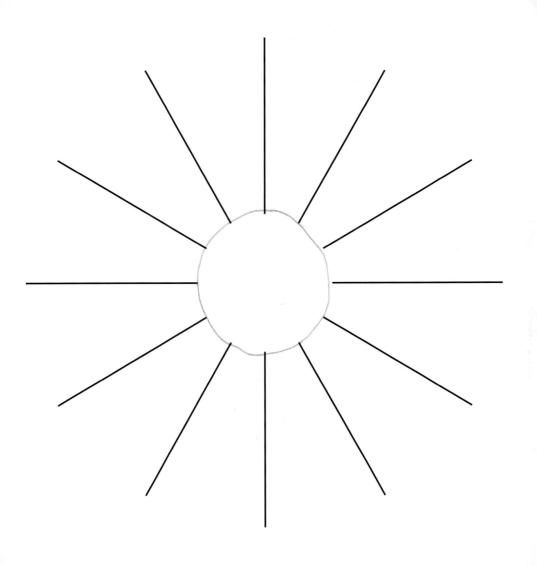

FRASER SPIRAL ILLUSION

The Fraser spiral illusion is an optical illusion that was first described by the British psychologist James Fraser in 1908. It is also known as the false spiral, or by its original name, the twisted cord illusion. The overlapping black arc segments appear to form a spiral; in reality, the arcs are a series of concentric circles. Although the Fraser spiral illusion and other similar illusions have not been completely explained, they has stimulated much valuable research into human perceptual processes.

Explanation

The visual distortion is produced by combining a regular line pattern (the circles) with misaligned parts (the differently colored strands or "twists"), an effect that is augmented by the spiral components of the background. The Zollner illusion and the cafe wall illusion, like many other visual effects, are based on a similar principle in which a sequence of tilted elements causes the eye to perceive an image incorrectly. The Fraser spiral illusion, along with other similar phenomena, is created by the way the retina and brain process the images.

HERMANN GRID ILLUSION

The Hermann grid illusion is an optical illusion reported by Ludimar Hermann in 1870. The illusion is characterised by "ghostlike" grey blobs perceived at the intersections of a white (or light-colored) grid on a black background. The grey blobs disappear when looking directly at an intersection.

How it works

Look at the left part of the diagram below and assume an on-center retinal ganglion cell. Its receptive field is indicated by the reddish disk. When the ganglion cell is, by chance, looking at the grating so that its centre ('+') is positioned at a crossing (left-top), there are 4 bright patches in the inhibitory surround. A ganglion cell looking at a street (left-bottom) however only gets 2 inhibitory patches, so it will have a higher spike rate then the one at the crossings.

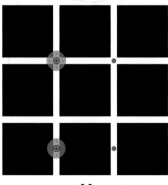

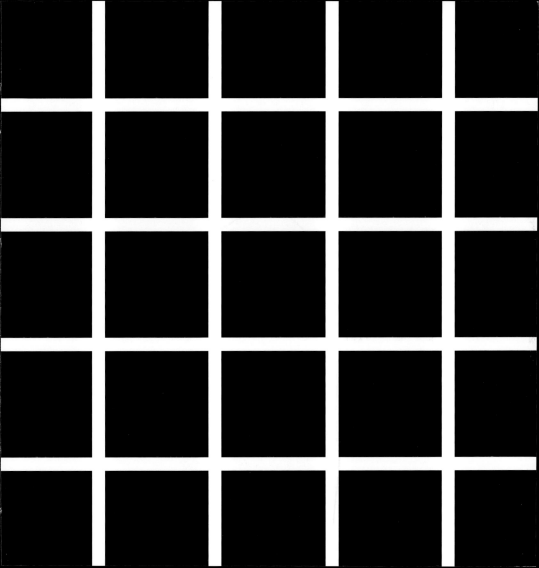

SCINTILLATING GRID ILLUSION

The scintillating grid illusion is an optical illusion, discovered by E. Lingelbach in 1994, that is usually considered a variation of the Hermann grid illusion.

It is constructed by superimposing white discs on the intersections of orthogonal gray bars on a black background. Dark dots seem to appear and disappear rapidly at random intersections, hence the label "scintillating". When a person keeps his or her eyes directly on a single intersection, the dark dot does not appear. The dark dots disappear if one is too close to or too far from the image.

Differences between the scintillating and Hermann grid illusions

The difference between the Hermann grid illusion and the scintillating illusion is that scintillating illusions have dots already in place at the intersection, whereas there are no dots already in place at the intersections of Hermann grid illusions. Since they are so similar, the two names are commonly used interchangeably. But the scintillating illusion does not occur with an isolated intersection, as in the case of the Hermann grid; observations suggest that a minimum of 3 × 3 evenly spaced intersections with superimposed discs are required to produce the effect. This requirement suggests the participation of global processes of the kind proposed for the linking and grouping of features in an image, in addition to local processes.

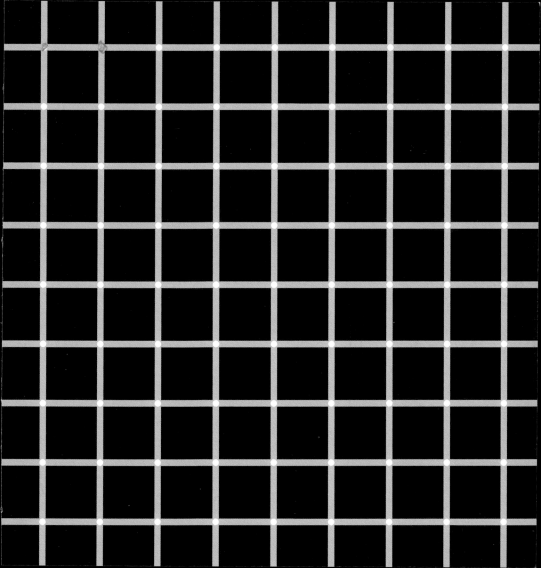

HERING ILLUSION

The Hering illusion is an optical illusion discovered by the German physiologist Ewald Hering in 1861. The two vertical lines are both straight, but they look as if they were bowing outwards. The distortion is produced by the lined pattern on the background, that simulates a perspective design, and creates a false impression of depth. The Orbison illusion is one of its variants, while the Wundt illusion produces a similar, but inverted effect. The Hering illusion looks like bike spokes around a central point, with vertical lines on either side of this central, so-called vanishing point. The illusion tricks us into thinking we are moving forward. Since we aren't actually moving and the figure is static, we misperceive the straight lines as curved ones.

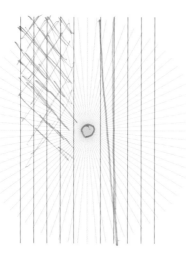

▶ The red lines appear to "bow" away from the radiating lines, even though they are perfectly straight

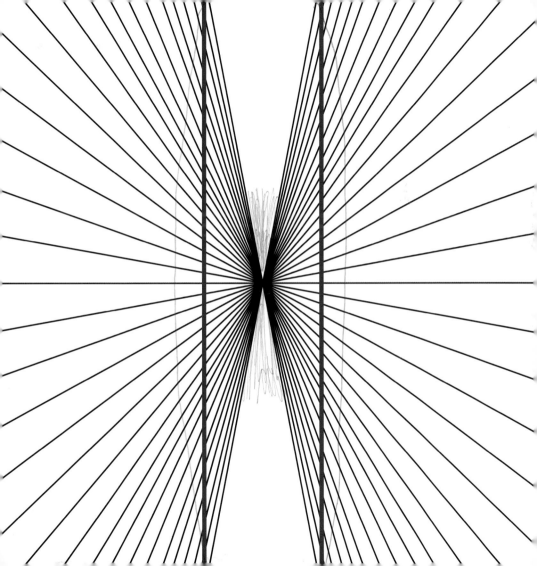

HYBRID IMAGE

A Hybrid Image is an optical illusion developed at MIT in which an image can be interpreted in one of two different ways depending on viewing distance. They achieve this through the way humans process visual input. Hybrid images change interpretation as a function of viewing distance. Hybrids combine the low-spatial frequencies of one picture with the high spatial frequencies of another picture producing an image with an interpretation that changes with viewing distance. Have a look at these two images and see what changes you can see.

◄► Have a look at these two images and see what happens when you either step back a few feet, or half shut your eyes

ISOMETRIC ILLUSION

An isometric illusion (also called an ambiguous figure or inside/outside illusion) is a type of optical illusion, specifically one due to multistable perception. In the example figure at right, the shape can be perceived as either an inside or an outside corner. In general, any shape built entirely of same-length (i.e., isometric) lines that does not clearly indicate relative direction between its components will evoke such a perceptual "flip-flopping".

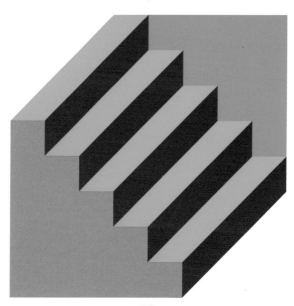

JASTROW ILLUSION

The Jastrow illusion is an optical illusion where two identical figures are placed next to each other. Although they are both exactly the same size, one appears to be larger.

The study of perceptual illusions like the Jastrow illusion helps scientists to investigate the various mechanisms involved in the visual perception of objects, and thus increases our understanding of how our minds function in informing us about the environment.

The Jastrow illusion is named for the American psychologist Joseph Jastrow, who discovered the illusion in 1889. Jastrow is also well known for his "duck-rabbit" ambiguous figure in which the the object's identification switches back and forth from that of a duck to that of a rabbit.

The Jastrow illusion is a size illusion where two curved shapes of identical measurements are placed next to each other. When viewing the two shapes, one looks significantly larger than the other. When the positions of the two shapes are reversed, the impression of which is the larger is also reversed.

Scientists are not yet certain what causes one figure in the Jastrow illusion to appear larger than the other. Similar effects have been noted by a number of researchers using a variety of geometric shapes, including trapezia, parallelograms, and lozenges.

The fact that the shorter side of one figure is next to the longer side of the other somehow tricks the brain into perceiving one shape as longer and the other as shorter, although it is unclear exactly why this is so.

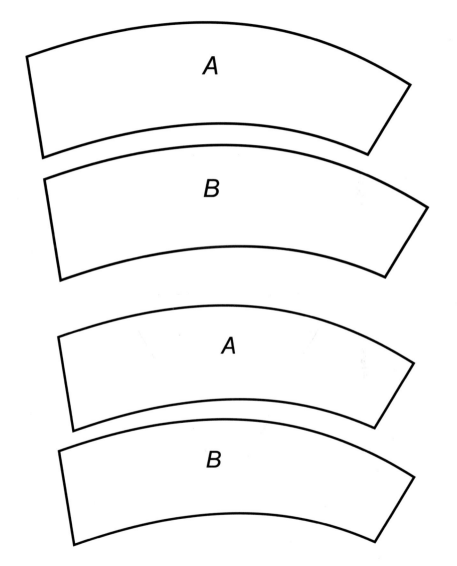

KANIZSA TRIANGLE

The Kanizsa triangle is an optical illusion first described by the Italian psychologist Gaetano Kanizsa in 1955. In the image below a white equilateral triangle is perceived, but in fact none is drawn. This effect is known as a subjective or illusory contour. Also, the nonexistent white triangle appears to be brighter than the surrounding area, but in fact it has the same brightness as the background.

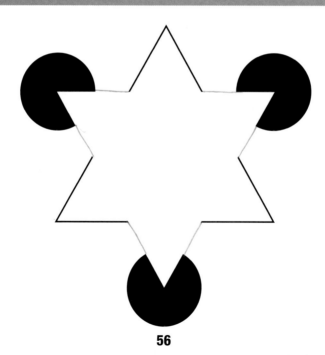

MACH BANDS

Mach bands are an optical illusion named after Ernst Mach consisting of an image of two wide bands, one light and one dark, separated by a narrow strip with a light-to-dark gradient. Humans perceive two narrow bands of different brightnesses either side of the gradient that are not present in the original image. The effect is like that of a spatial high-boost filter.

The illusion is usually supposed to be caused by lateral inhibition of the receptors in the eye. According to lateral inhibition, given that the gradient is horizontally oriented, the brain interprets the image as a collection of vertical lines. Every stripe has a value but the brain calculates the contrast of a stripe in relation to neighbor stripes. Stripes at the edges of the gradient have less lateral inhibition than the stripes in the uniform area so they appear as if they are brighter or darker than their real value.

ORBISON ILLUSION

An Orbison illusion is an optical illusion where straight lines appear distorted. Although the Orbison illusion and other similar illusions have not been completely explained, they have stimulated much valuable research into human perceptual processes.

The Orbison illusion is named after psychologist William Orbison, who first published his findings in a 1939 issue of the American Journal of Psychology. In addition to the figures that have taken his name, Orbison also included figures such as the Hering and Wundt illusions in his article, which discussed the potential cause of these sorts of illusions.

Orbison explained these illusions with the theory that fields of force were created in the perception of the background patterns. Any line that intersected these fields would be subsequently distorted in a predictable way. This theory, in the eyes of modern science, does not have much validity.

It is still unclear exactly what causes the figures to appear distorted. Theories involving the processing of angles by the brain have been suggested. Interactions between the neurons in the visual system may cause the perception of a distorted figure. Other theories suggest that the background gives an impression of perspective. As a result, the brain sees the shape of the figure as distorted.

▶ Due to the blue lines, the red square appears to be distorted

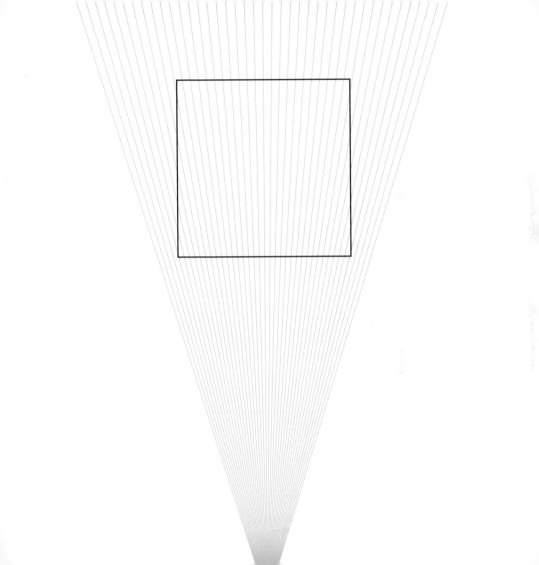

MCCOLLOUGH EFFECT

The McCollough effect is a phenomenon of human visual perception in which colorless gratings appear colored depending on the orientation of the gratings. It is an aftereffect requiring a period of induction to produce it. For example, if someone alternately looks at a red horizontal grating and a green vertical grating for a few minutes, a black-and-white horizontal grating will then look greenish and a black-and-white vertical grating will then look pinkish. The effect was discovered by Celeste McCollough in 1965.

To obtain the effect, first look at a test image on the opposite page (right). Next, stare alternately at the two induction images that appear on the next two pages. The left image shows horizontal grating with the colour red, and the other shows a green background with vertical grating (green being the opposite to red). Each image should be gazed at for several seconds at a time, and the two images should be gazed at for a total of several minutes for the effect to become visible. Stare approximately at the centre of each image, allowing the eyes to move around a little. After several minutes, look back to the image on the right; the gratings should appear tinted by the opposite colour to that of the induction gratings (i.e., horizontal should appear greenish and vertical pinkish).

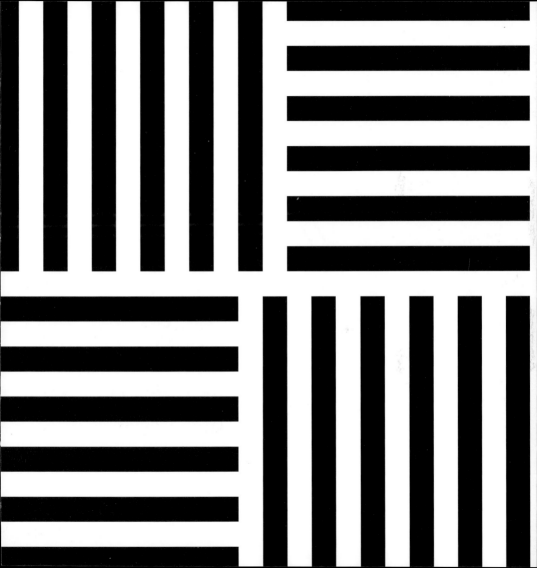

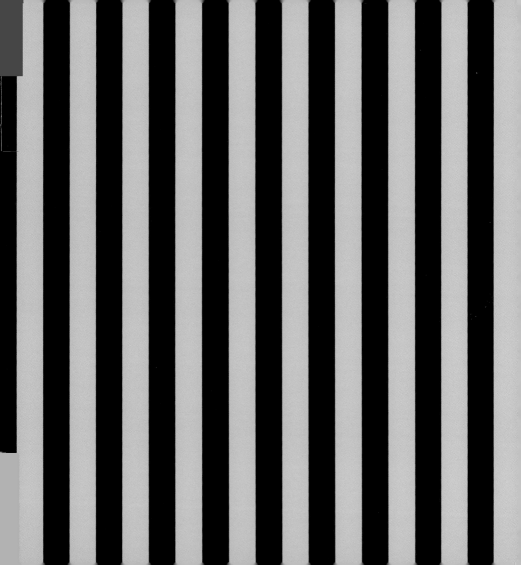

ILLUSORY MOTION

The term illusory motion, also known as motion illusion, is used to define the appearance of movement in a static image. This is an optical illusion in which a static image appears to be moving due to the cognitive effects of interacting color contrasts and shape position.

Another type of motion illusion that causes an optical illusion is when a moving object appears to be moving in a path other than what is perceived by the brain. A simple example of this can be demonstrated by placing a colored filter over one eye of an observer, and swinging a ball back and forth in front of them. To the observer the ball appears to be swinging in a circular motion.

MÜLLER-LYER ILLUSION

The Müller-Lyer illusion is an optical illusion consisting of nothing more than an arrow. When viewers are asked to place a mark on the figure at the mid-point, they invariably place it more towards the "tail" end. Another variation consists of two arrow-like figures, one with both ends pointing in, and the other with both ends pointing out. When asked to judge the lengths of the two lines, which are equal, viewers will typically claim that the line with inward pointing arrows is longer. One possible explanation is that you see the lines as three-dimensional, such as the outgoing and ingoing corners of a room. Another possible explanation is that the line with arrows pointing inwards may simply appear longer because the arrows themselves extend past the line.

The illusion is not cross-cultural. Non-Western subjects, and particularly subjects whose day-to-day surroundings are usually not rectangular (few buildings, doors, walls) are much less likely to be affected by it. Researchers discovered that the Zulu people, whose typical dwellings are circular thatched huts with no angular walls, were much less susceptible to the illusion.

▶ In the top image, the lines appear to be a different length. In the diagram below, highlighting the lines in red shows that they are in fact the same length

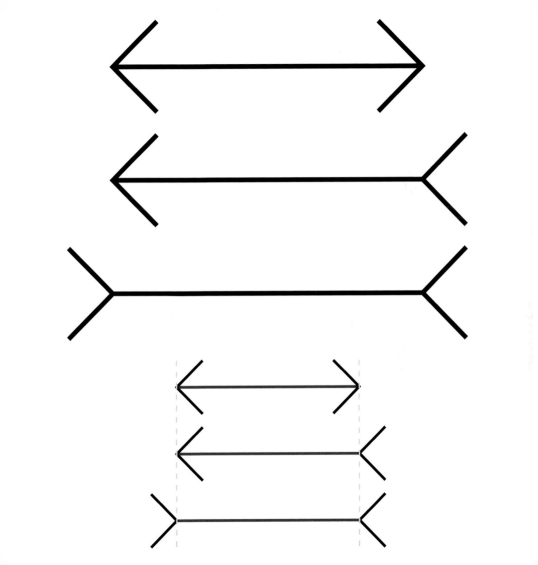

NECKER CUBE

The Necker Cube is an optical illusion first published in 1832 by Swiss crystallographer Louis Albert Necker. The Necker Cube is an ambiguous line drawing. It is a wire-frame drawing of a cube in oblique perspective, which means that parallel edges of the cube are drawn as parallel lines in the picture. When two lines cross, the picture does not show which is in front and which is behind. This makes the picture ambiguous; it can be interpreted two different ways. When a person stares at the picture, it will often seem to flip back and forth between the two valid interpretations (so-called multistable perception).

The effect is interesting because each part of the picture is ambiguous by itself, yet the human visual system picks an interpretation of each part that makes the whole consistent. The Necker Cube is sometimes used to test computer models of the human visual system to see whether they can arrive at consistent interpretations of the image the same way humans do.

Humans do not usually see an inconsistent interpretation of the cube. A cube whose edges cross in an inconsistent way is an example of an impossible object, specifically an impossible cube.

With the cube on the right, most people see the lower-left face as being in front most of the time. This is possibly because people view objects from above, with the top side visible, far more often than from below, with the bottom visible, so the brain "prefers" the interpretation that the cube is viewed from above.

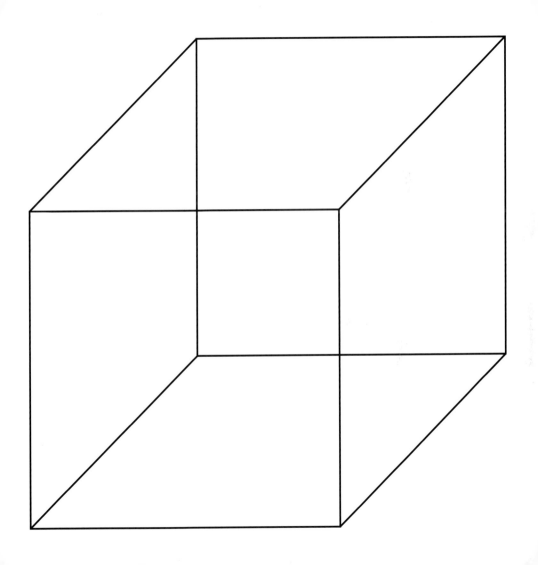

PENROSE TRIANGLE

The Penrose triangle, also known as the Penrose tribar, is an impossible object. It was first created by the Swedish artist Oscar Reutersvärd in 1934. The mathematician Roger Penrose independently devised and popularised it in the 1950s, describing it as "impossibility in its purest form". It is featured prominently in the works of artist M. C. Escher, whose earlier depictions of impossible objects partly inspired it.

The tribar appears to be a solid object, made of three straight beams of square cross-section which meet pairwise at right angles at the vertices of the triangle they form.

This combination of properties cannot be realized by any 3-dimensional object in ordinary Euclidean space. Such an object can exist in certain Euclidean 3-manifolds. There also exist 3-dimensional solid shapes each of which, when viewed from a certain angle, appears the same as the purple, green, and yellow 2-dimensional depiction of the Penrose triangle on this page.

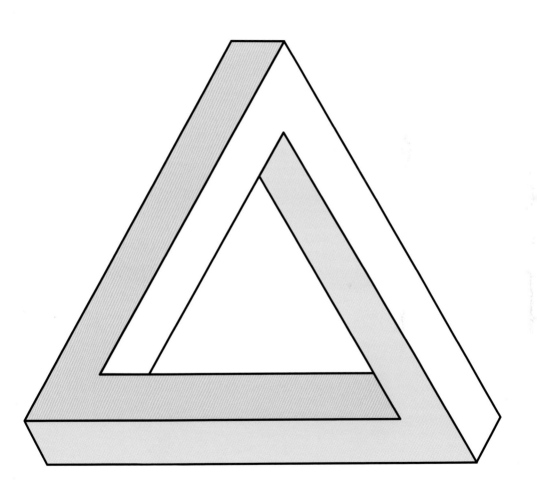

PERIPHERAL DRIFT

The peripheral drift illusion (PDI) refers to a motion illusion generated by the presentation of a sawtooth luminance grating in the visual periphery. This illusion was first described by Faubert and Herbert (1999), although a similar effect called the "escalator illusion" was reported by Fraser and Wilcox (1979). A variant of the PDI was created by Kitaoka and Ashida (2003) who took the continuous sawtooth luminance change, and reversed the intermediate greys. Kitaoka has created numerous variants of the PDI, and one called "rotating snakes" has become very popular. The latter demonstration has kindled great interest in the PDI.

The illusion is easily seen when fixating off to the side, and then blinking as fast as possible. Most observers see the illusion easily when reading text (such as on this page) with the illusion figure in the periphery. Motion is consistently perceived in a dark-to-light direction.

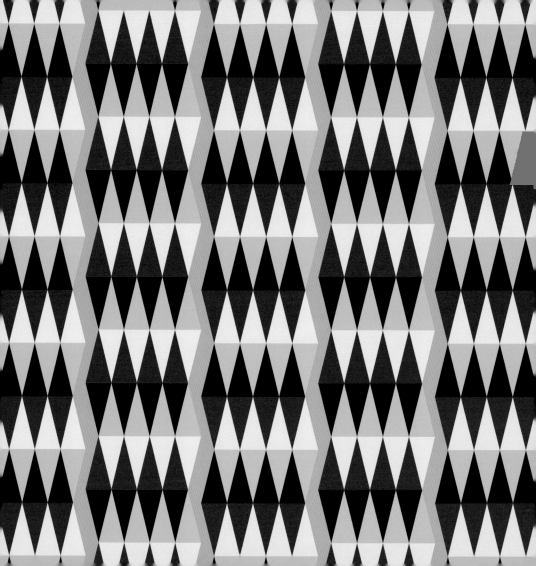

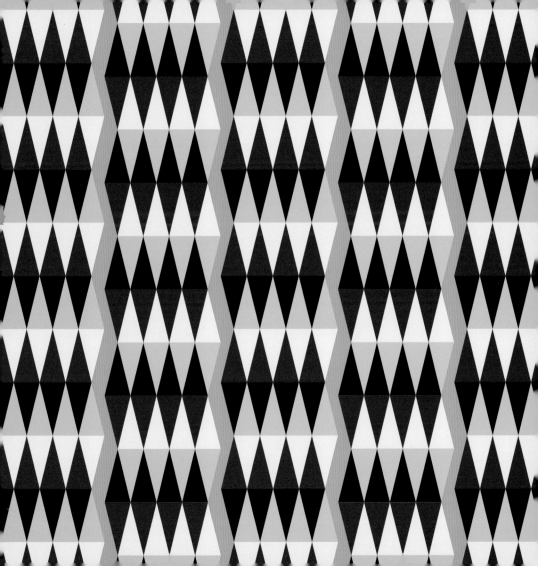

POGGENDORFF ILLUSION

The Poggendorff Illusion is an optical illusion that involves the brain's perception of the interaction between diagonal lines and horizontal and vertical edges. It is named after Poggendorff, who discovered it in the drawing of Johann Karl Friedrich Zöllner, in which Zöllner showed the Zöllner illusion in 1860.

In the picture to the right, a straight black and red line is obscured by a grey rectangle. The blue line, rather than the red line, appears to be a continuation of the black one, which is clearly shown not to be the case on the second picture below.

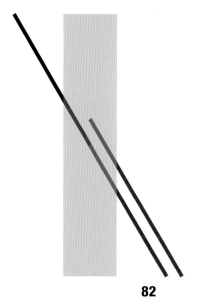

◀ When we make the rectangle transparent, the illusion is destroyed showing that the red line is in fact the continuation and not the blue one

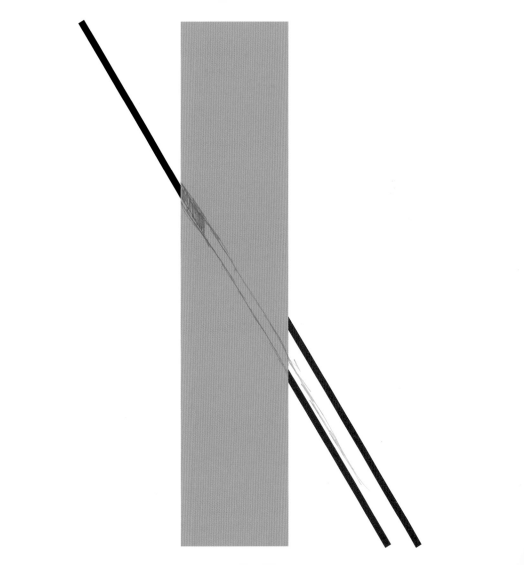

PONZO ILLUSION

The Ponzo illusion is an optical illusion that was first demonstrated by the Italian psychologist Mario Ponzo in 1913. He suggested that the human mind judges an object's size based on its background. He showed this by drawing two identical lines across a pair of converging lines, similar to railway tracks. The upper line looks longer because we interpret the converging sides according to linear perspective as parallel lines receding into the distance.

One of the explanations for Ponzo illusion is the 'Perspective hypothesis', which states that the perspective feature in the figure is obviously produced by the converging lines ordinarily associated with distance, that is, the two oblique lines appear to converge toward the horizon or a vanishing point.

◀ The red lines in this diagram illustrate the fact that despite the illusion on the right, both of the yellow lines are in fact the same width.

RUBIN VASE

Rubin's vase (sometimes known as the Rubin face or the Figure-ground vase) is a famous set of cognitive optical illusions developed around 1915 by the Danish psychologist Edgar Rubin.

The illusion generally presents the viewer with a mental choice of two interpretations, each of which is valid. Often, the viewer sees only one of them, and only realizes the second, valid, interpretation after some time or prompting. When they attempt to simultaneously see the second and first interpretations, they suddenly cannot see the first interpretation anymore, and no matter how they try, they simply cannot encompass both interpretations simultaneously - one occludes the other.

Explanation

The illusions are useful because they are an excellent and intuitive demonstration of the figure-ground distinction the brain makes during visual perception. Rubin's figure-ground distinction, since it involved higher-level cognitive pattern matching, in which the overall picture determines its mental interpretation, rather than the net effect of the individual pieces, influenced the Gestalt psychologists, who discovered many similar illusions themselves.

Normally the brain classifies images by what surrounds what - establishing depth and relationships. If something surrounds another thing, the surrounded object is seen as figure, and the presumably further away (and hence background) object is the ground, and vice versa.

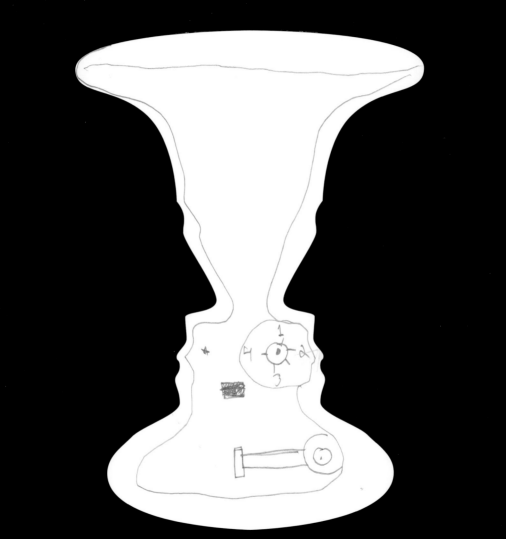

SAME COLOUR ILLUSION

The same color illusion—also known as Adelson's checker shadow illusion, checker shadow illusion and checker shadow—is an optical illusion published by Edward H. Adelson, Professor of Vision Science at MIT in 1995. The squares A and B on the illusion are the same color (or shade), although they seem to be different. This can be proven by sampling the colors of A and B in an image-editing program, which will show that they are in fact the same color. By erasing everything except the two labelled squares, the effect of the illusion can be removed.

◀ Connecting the two squares marked "A" and "B" shows that they are actually the same colour

WHITE'S ILLUSION

White's illusion is an optical illusion illustrating the fact that the same target luminance can elicit different perceptions of brightness in different contexts.

Although the gray rectangles are all of equal luminance, the ones seen in the context with the dark stripes appear brighter than the ones seen in the context with the bright stripes. This effect is opposite to what would be expected from a simple physiological explanation on the basis of simultaneous contrast (in that case the rectangles sharing the long borders with the dark stripes should appear brighter).

To see that the gray bars are the same color, you can stare at the image until your eyes begin to cross, then control your eyes until the gray bars line up, making one big gray bar, proving that the gray bars are the same color.

▼ In the image below, the two grey squares are exactly identical in colour and size.

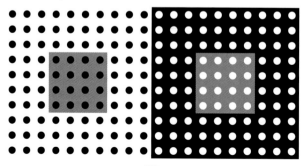

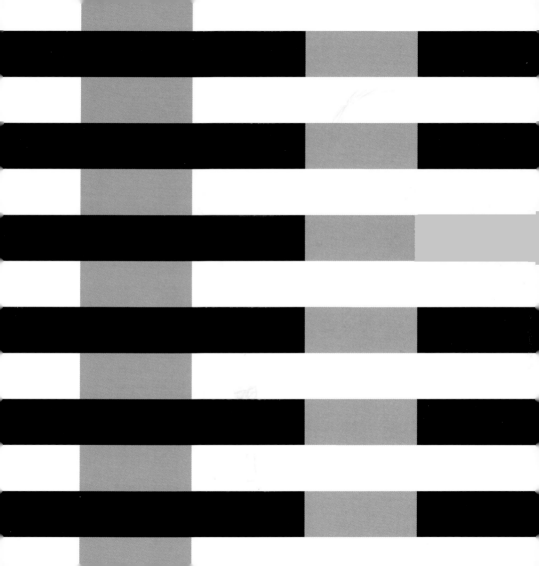

WUNDT ILLUSION

The Wundt illusion is an optical illusion that was first described by the German psychologist Wilhelm Wundt in the 19th century. The two red vertical lines are both straight, but they may look as if they are bowed inwards to some observers. The distortion is induced by the crooked lines on the background, as in Orbison's illusion. The Hering illusion produces a similar, but inverted effect. Another variant of the Wundt illusion is the Horizontal-Vertical Illusion, introduced by Wundt on 1858. The two intersecting lines are equal in length although the vertical line appears to be much longer. The horizontal line needs to be extended up to 30% to match the perceptual length of the vertical line. This is not confined to simple line drawings, as this can also be seen in buildings, parking meters, as well as other things viewed in a natural setting.

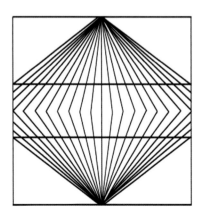

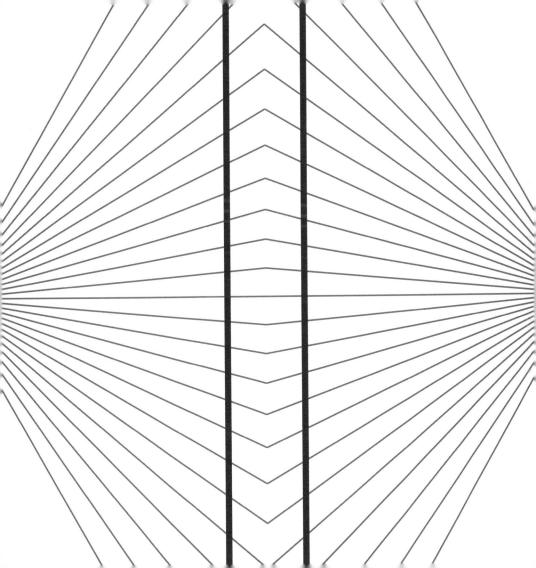

ZOLNER ILLUSION

The Zöllner illusion is a classic optical illusion named after its discoverer, German astrophysicist Johann Karl Friedrich Zöllner. In 1860, Zöllner sent his discovery in a letter to physicist and scholar Johann Christian Poggendorff, editor of Annalen der Physik und Chemie, who subsequently discovered the related Poggendorff illusion, in the original drawing of Zöllner.

In this figure the black lines seem to be unparallel, but in reality they are parallel. The shorter lines are on an angle to the longer lines. This angle helps to create the impression that one end of the longer lines is nearer to us than the other end. This is very similar to the way the Wundt illusion appears. It may be that the Zöllner illusion is caused by this impression of depth.

It is interesting to see what happens when the colours in this illusion are changed. If the illusion is printed in green on a red background and the red and green are equally bright, the illusion disappears.

This illusion is similar to the Hering illusion, the Poggendorff illusion and the Müller-Lyer illusion. All these illusions demonstrate how lines can seem to be distorted by their background.

INDEX